LISTENING AND REMEMBERING SPECIFIC DETAILS

Jean Gilliam DeGaetano
Illustrations by Kevin N. Newman

Great Ideas for Teaching · P.O. Box 444 · Wrightsville Beach · NC · 28480

ISBN 1-886143-37-4

LISTENING AND REMEMBERING SPECIFIC DETAILS

Jean Gilliam DeGaetano

The goals for the activities in this unit are to listen to short stories, to retain the important details in the stories, and to be able to accurately answer questions about the stories.

The unit has 30 activity lessons with a corresponding instructor's manual for each lesson. Each lesson has two stories that are to be read aloud to the students. For the first story, the large picture provides visual clues for remembering specific details in that story. Before reading the story aloud, the students will be told three things to remember while the story is being read. After the story has been read, the students will be asked five questions about the story. Following the same procedure, the second story will be read. The difference between the two stories is that the second story has no picture because the story is about a sequential event that has not yet happened.

The pages in this unit are masters that are to be used to make additional copies for the students. The masters should not be consumed. It is recommended, for your convenience, that copies of all lessons be made and filed prior to using this unit.

Directions are provided on each instructor's worksheet enabling the professional to use the unit without prior preparation. These not only serve as a manual for the professional but also inform the parents as to how the activities were presented in class or how they can be used to review the work or as a homework assignment.

The unit can be used with individual students or in groups. While only one student is addressed at a time, group lessons allow the other students to listen and observe the questions and responses of classmates.

When sending work home, the note below may be copied and attached to the student's worksheet and the instructor's worksheet.

Student's Name: _____

The purpose of this activity is to learn to listen for specific details in stories. There are two stories in each lesson. The first story has a picture to help the students remember specific details. The second story does not have a picture because it is about something that has not happened. Before beginning, each student should be given three clues about what they are to remember in each story. After listening to the story, they will be asked five questions about each story. Three of the questions match the clues given before the story was read. The other two are surprise questions. The instructor's page is attached to the student copy for home review. Thank you if you will review this lesson at home.

_____

STUDENT WORKSHEET

ANN'S BIRTHDAY PARTY

INSTRUCTOR'S WORKSHEET

INSTRUCTOR'S DIRECTIONS:

Before beginning, the instructor should give each student the worksheet that corresponds to the instructor's worksheet. Before reading Story #1, the instructor should ask the students to listen carefully to three questions and remember the information as the story is read. The instructor then reads the story aloud. After the story is read, the instructor asks the same three questions along with two additional questions for the students to answer aloud. Their large picture should provide visual clues. In Story #2, the same process is repeated, keeping in mind that the questions and story do not refer directly to the picture.

ANN'S BIRTHDAY PARTY

Story #1 (Pictured)

Things to remember:

1. Who is having a birthday?
2. How old is Ann?
3. What is special about her cake?

Ann is having a birthday party. She is six-years-old today. Ann told her mother she would like a very special cake for her sixth birthday. She said she wanted a birthday cake with three layers: a large layer on the bottom, a medium-sized layer in the middle and a small layer on top. She is very happy because her mother baked her a cake exactly like she wanted.

Questions:

1. Who is having a birthday?
2. How old is Ann?
3. What is special about her cake?
4. What does her cake look like?
5. Does she like her cake?

Story #2: (Not Pictured)

Things to remember:

1. Did many people come to her party?
2. What was her favorite gift?
3. Did her grandparents come?

Ann's party was so much fun. Ten of her classmates came to it. They gave her wonderful gifts. The one she loved the best was a big beachball that her friend Barbara gave to her. She plans to take it on vacation when she goes to the beach. Ann's grandparents also came. They gave her a new pair of roller skates. They loved her birthday cake and took a picture of it.

Questions:

1. Did many people come to her party?
2. What was her favorite gift?
3. Did her grandparents come?
4. What did they give her?
5. Did they like her cake? How do you know?

PICKING FLOWERS FOR GRANDMA

INSTRUCTOR'S WORKSHEET

INSTRUCTOR'S DIRECTIONS:

Before beginning, the instructor should give each student the worksheet that corresponds to the instructor's worksheet. Before reading Story #1, the instructor should ask the students to listen carefully to three questions and remember the information as the story is read. The instructor then reads the story aloud. After the story is read, the instructor asks the same three questions along with two additional questions for the students to answer aloud. Their large picture should provide visual clues. In Story #2, the same process is repeated, keeping in mind that the questions and story do not refer directly to the picture.

PICKING FLOWERS FOR GRANDMA

Story #1 (Pictured)

Things to remember:

1. Who is having company?
2. Where will Beth pick flowers?
3. Why is Beth picking flowers?

It is a beautiful spring day. Beth is going to have company. Her grandmother is coming to visit. Beth wants to give her a wonderful surprise. She asks her mother's permission to pick some flowers from the garden. Her mother gives her a basket for the flowers. Beth picks the prettiest flowers in the garden.

Questions:

1. Who is having company?
2. Who is coming to visit Beth?
3. Why is Beth picking flowers?
4. Where will Beth pick flowers?
5. What did Beth's mother give her to put the flowers in?

Story #2: (Not Pictured)

Things to remember:

1. How many flowers did Beth pick?
2. What colors were the flowers?
3. What did Beth do with the flowers?

Beth picked a whole basket of flowers. The flowers were pink, yellow and purple. She brought them into her house and asked her mother for something pretty to put them in. Her mother gave her a beautiful vase with a bird on it. Beth's grandmother was very happy when she saw the beautiful flowers Beth had picked for her.

Questions:

1. How many flowers did Beth pick?
2. What colors were the flowers?
3. Where did Beth take the flowers after she picked them?
4. What did Beth do with the flowers?
5. Who was very happy when she saw the flowers?

STUDENT WORKSHEET

GETTING READY FOR SCHOOL

INSTRUCTOR'S WORKSHEET

INSTRUCTOR'S DIRECTIONS:

Before beginning, the instructor should give each student the worksheet that corresponds to the instructor's worksheet. Before reading Story #1, the instructor should ask the students to listen carefully to three questions and remember the information as the story is read. The instructor then reads the story aloud. After the story is read, the instructor asks the same three questions along with two additional questions for the students to answer aloud. Their large picture should provide visual clues. In Story #2, the same process is repeated, keeping in mind that the questions and story do not refer directly to the picture.

GETTING READY FOR SCHOOL

Story #1 (Pictured)

Things to remember:

1. Who woke up early?
2. What did Mary put on her feet?
3. Why is today a special day for Mary?

Today is a special day for Mary. She woke up early and climbed out of bed. She put on her funny bunny slippers and went into the bathroom. After she washed her face, she brushed her teeth. She used the new toothbrush and toothpaste her mother had bought for her. It is a special day because it is Mary's first day of school.

Questions:

1. Who woke up early?
2. What did Mary put on her feet?
3. What did Mary do after she washed her face?
4. Is Mary's toothbrush new or old?
5. Why is today a special day for Mary?

Story #2: (Not Pictured)

Things to remember:

1. What did Mary wear to school?
2. What did she put her pencils and papers in?
3. How did Mary get to school?

Mary's first day of school was so much fun. She wore a new dress and a pretty bow in her hair. Her mother and father had bought her a new book bag to carry her pencils and papers in and a new lunch box. Best of all, she rode the bus with her best friend, Sally. Mary was a very happy girl.

Questions:

1. What did Mary wear to school?
2. What did she put in her hair?
3. What did she put her pencils and papers in?
4. How did Mary get to school?
5. Who rode the school bus with her?

ROVER GETS A BATH

INSTRUCTOR'S WORKSHEET

INSTRUCTOR'S DIRECTIONS:

Before beginning, the instructor should give each student the worksheet that corresponds to the instructor's worksheet. Before reading Story #1, the instructor should ask the students to listen carefully to three questions and remember the information as the story is read. The instructor then reads the story aloud. After the story is read, the instructor asks the same three questions along with two additional questions for the students to answer aloud. Their large picture should provide visual clues. In Story #2, the same process is repeated, keeping in mind that the questions and story do not refer directly to the picture.

ROVER GETS A BATH

Story #1 (Pictured)

Things to remember:

1. When did Rover go outside to play?
2. What did Rover jump in?
3. What did Tommy use to wash Rover?

Rover went outside to play after it had rained. There were many mud puddles and Rover jumped in all of them. There was mud all over Rover. Tommy was upset when he saw Rover. He filled a big bucket full of soapy water and gave Rover a bath. He used lots of soap because Rover was very dirty.

Questions:

1. When did Rover go outside to play?
2. What did Rover jump in?
3. Was Tommy happy when he saw Rover?
4. Where did Tommy wash Rover?
5. What did Tommy use to wash Rover?

Story #2: (Not Pictured)

Things to remember:

1. What did Tommy use to dry Rover?
2. Why did Rover start barking?
3. What did Tommy do so that Rover could not jump in anymore mud puddles?

After Rover got out of the bucket, Tommy dried him with a great big towel. Then he brushed his fur and put a new collar around Rover's neck. Rover began to bark because he wanted to go back outside to play. Tommy took Rover outside but this time he put a leash around Rover's neck.

Questions:

1. Was Rover wet or dry when he got out of the bucket?
2. What did Tommy use to dry Rover?
3. What did Tommy do after he dried Rover?
4. Why did Rover start barking?
5. What did Tommy do so that Rover could not jump in anymore mud puddles?

MOLLY'S NEW PET

INSTRUCTOR'S WORKSHEET

INSTRUCTOR'S DIRECTIONS:

Before beginning, the instructor should give each student the worksheet that corresponds to the instructor's worksheet. Before reading Story #1, the instructor should ask the students to listen carefully to three questions and remember the information as the story is read. The instructor then reads the story aloud. After the story is read, the instructor asks the same three questions along with two additional questions for the students to answer aloud. Their large picture should provide visual clues. In Story #2, the same process is repeated, keeping in mind that the questions and story do not refer directly to the picture.

MOLLY'S NEW PET

Story #1 (Pictured)

Things to remember:

1. Why did Molly get a new pet?
2. Where did Molly get her new pet?
3. What kind of pet did Molly get?

Molly got all A's on her report card. Her mom and dad said she could get a new pet. They went to the pet store so Molly could pick out her new pet. Molly looked at all the puppies, the kittens and the goldfish but she didn't see anything she wanted. Then she heard a chirping sound coming from a little bird in a cage. The bird chirped and chirped at Molly. Molly knew the bird was the perfect pet for her.

Questions:

1. Why did Molly get a new pet?
2. Where did Molly get her new pet?
3. Did Molly want a puppy or a kitten?
4. What kind of sound did Molly hear?
5. What kind of pet did Molly get?

Story #2: (Not Pictured)

Things to remember:

1. Where did Molly put her new bird?
2. What happened when Molly opened the cage?
3. Who caught the bird and put it back in its cage?

Molly brought her new bird home. She put its cage in her room so she could see the little bird every morning. She opened the cage so the little bird could fly around her room. It flew down the stairs and all around the living room. Finally, Molly's dad caught the bird and put it back in its cage. He told Molly not to open the cage anymore.

Questions:

1. Where did Molly put her new bird?
2. Why did Molly open the cage?
3. What happened when Molly opened the cage?
4. Where did the bird fly?
5. Who caught the bird and put it back in its cage?

COOKING BREAKFAST FOR MOM AND DAD

INSTRUCTOR'S WORKSHEET

INSTRUCTOR'S DIRECTIONS:

Before beginning, the instructor should give each student the worksheet that corresponds to the instructor's worksheet. Before reading Story #1, the instructor should ask the students to listen carefully to three questions and remember the information as the story is read. The instructor then reads the story aloud. After the story is read, the instructor asks the same three questions along with two additional questions for the students to answer aloud. Their large picture should provide visual clues. In Story #2, the same process is repeated, keeping in mind that the questions and story do not refer directly to the picture.

COOKING BREAKFAST FOR MOM AND DAD

Story #1 (Pictured)

Things to remember:

1. How does Debbie surprise her mom and dad?
2. What is their favorite breakfast?
3. What does she cook the bacon and eggs in?

Debbie wants to surprise her mom and dad by cooking breakfast. Their favorite breakfast is bacon and eggs. She takes the bacon and eggs out of the refrigerator and puts them in the frying pan. She puts on an apron so she won't mess up her clothes. Debbie uses a spatula to turn the bacon and eggs. When everything is done, she puts the bacon and eggs on plates for her mom and dad.

Questions:

1. How does Debbie surprise her mom and dad?
2. What is their favorite breakfast?
3. Where does Debbie get the bacon and eggs?
4. What does she cook the bacon and eggs in?
5. What does she wear to keep her clothes clean?

Story #2: (Not Pictured)

Things to remember:

1. What did Debbie do after she fixed breakfast?
2. Where did she wash the dishes?
3. What did Debbie use to clean the table?

After Debbie fixed her parent's breakfast, she decided she would clean the kitchen. She took the dishes off the table and put them in the sink. She filled the sink with soapy water, washed the dishes and then dried them. When she was through, Debbie took a cloth and wiped the crumbs off the table. Her mom and dad gave her a hug and kiss for being such a good girl.

Questions:

1. What did Debbie do after she fixed breakfast?
2. Where did she wash the dishes?
3. Did she use soapy water or slimy water to wash the dishes?
4. What did Debbie use to clean the table?
5. What did her mom and dad do?

BILLY AND JOEY GO FISHING

INSTRUCTOR'S WORKSHEET

INSTRUCTOR'S DIRECTIONS:

Before beginning, the instructor should give each student the worksheet that corresponds to the instructor's worksheet. Before reading Story #1, the instructor should ask the students to listen carefully to three questions and remember the information as the story is read. The instructor then reads the story aloud. After the story is read, the instructor asks the same three questions along with two additional questions for the students to answer aloud. Their large picture should provide visual clues. In Story #2, the same process is repeated, keeping in mind that the questions and story do not refer directly to the picture.

BILLY AND JOEY GO FISHING

Story #1 (Pictured)

Things to remember:

1. What kind of day was it?
2. What were Billy and Joey going to do?
3. Where was the perfect place to fish?

It was a beautiful sunny day. Billy and Joey decided to go fishing. They got their fishing poles and went to their favorite fishing spot. They looked for the best place to fish. Billy saw the best place to fish - a log that had fallen across a stream. They could sit on the log and watch the fish swimming by. It was the perfect place to fish.

Questions:

1. What kind of day was it?
2. What were Billy and Joey going to do?
3. Where was the perfect place to fish?
4. What did they bring to catch a fish?
5. What could Billy and Joey see in the water?

Story #2: (Not Pictured)

Things to remember:

1. How long did Billy and Joey fish?
2. What size fish did they take home?
3. Why were they going to take the fish home?

Billy and Joey fished all day. They caught big fish and little fish. They threw the little fish back in the water but kept all of the big fish to take home for dinner. They fished until they ran out of worms. Then they decided it was time to go home. They put the fish in a big bucket to take home to Billy's mom so she could cook the fish for dinner.

Questions:

1. How long did Billy and Joey fish?
2. Do you think they caught a few or a lot of fish?
3. What size fish did they take home?
4. Why did they decide to stop fishing?
5. Why were they going to take the fish home?

STUDENT WORKSHEET

WASHING THE DISHES

INSTRUCTOR'S WORKSHEET

INSTRUCTOR'S DIRECTIONS:

Before beginning, the instructor should give each student the worksheet that corresponds to the instructor's worksheet. Before reading Story #1, the instructor should ask the students to listen carefully to three questions and remember the information as the story is read. The instructor then reads the story aloud. After the story is read, the instructor asks the same three questions along with two additional questions for the students to answer aloud. Their large picture should provide visual clues. In Story #2, the same process is repeated, keeping in mind that the questions and story do not refer directly to the picture.

WASHING THE DISHES

Story #1 (Pictured)

Things to remember:

1. Why did Karen wash and dry the dishes?
2. Where did she wash the dishes?
3. What did she use to dry the dishes?

Karen had to wash and dry the dishes because the dishwasher was broken. She put the dishes in a dishpan filled with soap and water. Then she washed them with a sponge. After she washed them, she put them in the drainer on the kitchen counter. After she washed all the dishes, she dried them with a new dish towel.

Questions:

1. Why did Karen wash and dry the dishes?
2. Where did she wash the dishes?
3. Did she dry the dishes before or after she washed them?
4. Where did she put the dishes after she washed them?
5. What did she use to dry the dishes?

Story #2: (Not Pictured)

Things to remember:

1. What did Karen do after she washed and dried the dishes?
2. Where did she put the dishes?
3. What did she stand on to reach the cabinet?

After Karen washed and dried the dishes, she put them in the cabinet above the sink. Karen had to stand on a chair to reach the cabinet. She was very careful and put the dishes away one at a time. After the dishes were put away, she put away the dish drainer and wiped the counter with a clean cloth.

Questions:

1. What did Karen do after she washed and dried the dishes?
2. Where did she put the dishes?
3. Was the cabinet high or low?
4. What did she stand on to reach the cabinet?
5. What did she do after all the dishes were put away?

STUDENT WORKSHEET

VISITING GRANDFATHER'S FARM

INSTRUCTOR'S WORKSHEET

INSTRUCTOR'S DIRECTIONS:

Before beginning, the instructor should give each student the worksheet that corresponds to the instructor's worksheet. Before reading Story #1, the instructor should ask the students to listen carefully to three questions and remember the information as the story is read. The instructor then reads the story aloud. After the story is read, the instructor asks the same three questions along with two additional questions for the students to answer aloud. Their large picture should provide visual clues. In Story #2, the same process is repeated, keeping in mind that the questions and story do not refer directly to the picture.

VISITING GRANDFATHER'S FARM

Story #1 (Pictured)

Things to remember:

1. Where are Jimmy and Jennifer going?
2. Why do they like to go to their grandfather's farm?
3. What color are the baby chicks?

Jimmy and Jennifer are visiting their grandfather's farm. They like to go to the farm so they can play with the baby chicks. Their grandfather has lots of chicks. They are soft and yellow and so tiny they can fit in Jimmy's hands. Jimmy and Jennifer are very careful when they pet the chicks because they do not want to hurt them.

Questions:

1. Where are Jimmy and Jennifer going?
2. Why do they like to go to their grandfather's farm?
3. What color are the baby chicks?
4. Are the baby chicks soft or scratchy?
5. Why are Jimmy and Jennifer careful when they pick up the baby chicks?

Story #2: (Not Pictured)

Things to remember:

1. Where did Jimmy and Jennifer go after they played with the baby chicks?
2. What did they see in the barn?
3. What sound did the cows make?

After Jimmy and Jennifer played with the baby chicks, they went to the barn. They wanted to see the cows and horses. They walked up and down the barn, stopping to pet each of the animals they saw. The cows mooed when they touched their heads. Then they went outside to pick apples with their grandfather.

Questions:

1. Where did Jimmy and Jennifer go after they played with the baby chicks?
2. What did they see in the barn?
3. What did they do when they saw the animals?
4. What sound did the cows make?
5. What did they pick with their grandfather?

BILLY'S SUMMER JOB

INSTRUCTOR'S WORKSHEET

INSTRUCTOR'S DIRECTIONS:

Before beginning, the instructor should give each student the worksheet that corresponds to the instructor's worksheet. Before reading Story #1, the instructor should ask the students to listen carefully to three questions and remember the information as the story is read. The instructor then reads the story aloud. After the story is read, the instructor asks the same three questions along with two additional questions for the students to answer aloud. Their large picture should provide visual clues. In Story #2, the same process is repeated, keeping in mind that the questions and story do not refer directly to the picture.

BILLY'S SUMMER JOB

Story #1 (Pictured)

Things to remember:

1. What kind of summer job does Billy have?
2. What does Billy want to buy?
3. Where does he put his money at the end of the day?

Billy has a summer job mowing lawns. He wants to save enough money to buy a new blue bicycle. Each day he mows one lawn in the neighborhood. Some yards are very big, some are very little. If the yard is big, he makes a lot of money. If the yard is little, he makes a little money. At the end of each day he puts the money he earned in his piggy bank.

Questions:

1. What kind of summer job does Billy have?
2. What does Billy want to buy?
3. What color bicycle does Billy want?
4. What size are the yards that Billy mows?
5. Where does he put his money at the end of the day?

Story #2: (Not Pictured)

Things to remember:

1. Was it a short time or a long time before Billy had enough money to buy a bicycle?
2. Where did his father take him?
3. What did his bicycle look like?

It was a long time before Billy had enough money to buy a new bicycle. His father took him to the bicycle store. Billy looked at all the bicycles until he found the one he wanted. It was blue with a white stripe. It had a basket to hold the newspapers he delivered every morning before school. He paid his money and rode his bicycle out of the store.

Questions:

1. Was it a short time or a long time before Billy had enough money to buy a bicycle?
2. Where did his father take him?
3. What color was the bicycle?
4. What did the bicycle have on the front of it?
5. What will Billy put into the basket?

STUDENT WORKSHEET

HAVING AN AFTERNOON SNACK

INSTRUCTOR'S WORKSHEET

INSTRUCTOR'S DIRECTIONS:

Before beginning, the instructor should give each student the worksheet that corresponds to the instructor's worksheet. Before reading Story #1, the instructor should ask the students to listen carefully to three questions and remember the information as the story is read. The instructor then reads the story aloud. After the story is read, the instructor asks the same three questions along with two additional questions for the students to answer aloud. Their large picture should provide visual clues. In Story #2, the same process is repeated, keeping in mind that the questions and story do not refer directly to the picture.

HAVING AN AFTERNOON SNACK

Story #1 (Pictured)

Things to remember:

1. Why did Jane invite Mike to her house?
2. What did Jane's mother bake?
3. Where did they eat their snacks?

Jane invited Mike to come over to her house after school for an afternoon snack. Jane's mother baked her favorite chocolate chip cookies. There were so many chips in the cookies, Jane and Mike could not count them. Jane's mother gave each of them one cookie and a glass of milk. They took their snacks out on the porch and sat on two little stools.

Questions:

1. Why did Jane invite Mike to her house?
2. What did Jane's mother bake?
3. Were there a lot or a few chocolate chips in the cookies?
4. What did they drink with their cookies?
5. Where did they eat their snacks?

Story #2: (Not Pictured)

Things to remember:

1. What did Jane and Mike want to do after they ate their snacks?
2. Where did they want to watch TV?
3. What did Jane need to do after she watched TV?

After they ate their snacks, Jane and Mike decided to watch TV. They asked Jane's mother if they could watch TV in the family room. She said they could only watch one show because Jane needed to do her homework. They hurried to the family room since they didn't want to miss their favorite show.

Questions:

1. What did Jane and Mike want to do after they ate their snacks?
2. Who gave them permission to watch TV?
3. Where did they want to watch TV?
4. How many shows were they allowed to watch?
5. What did Jane need to do after she watched TV?

BOBBY'S SCIENCE PROJECT

INSTRUCTOR'S WORKSHEET

INSTRUCTOR'S DIRECTIONS:

Before beginning, the instructor should give each student the worksheet that corresponds to the instructor's worksheet. Before reading Story #1, the instructor should ask the students to listen carefully to three questions and remember the information as the story is read. The instructor then reads the story aloud. After the story is read, the instructor asks the same three questions along with two additional questions for the students to answer aloud. Their large picture should provide visual clues. In Story #2, the same process is repeated, keeping in mind that the questions and story do not refer directly to the picture.

BOBBY'S SCIENCE PROJECT

Story #1 (Pictured)

Things to remember:

1. What kind of project is Bobby working on?
2. What did he decide to collect?
3. Where did he find the caterpillars?

Bobby is working on a science project. He is collecting caterpillars. His mother gave him a glass jar to put them in. Bobby went outside and looked everywhere for caterpillars. He did not find any in the grass or on the sidewalk. He found some in the tree in his backyard. He picked them off the tree one at a time and put them into the jar. He knew Miss Jones would be happy with his project.

Questions:

1. What kind of project is Bobby working on?
2. What did he decide to collect?
3. What is he going to put the caterpillars in?
4. Who gave him the glass jar?
5. Where did he find the caterpillars?

Story #2: (Not Pictured)

Things to remember:

1. Where did Bobby take his science project?
2. What did Bobby do with the jar of caterpillars?
3. What did the class decide to do with the caterpillars?

Bobby took his science project to school the next day. Miss Jones was very happy. She asked Bobby to tell the class about caterpillars and how they become butterflies. Bobby passed the jar around the classroom so that everyone could see the caterpillars. The class decided to put the caterpillars into a warm dark place to see if they turned into butterflies. This became their next science project.

Questions:

1. Where did Bobby take his science project?
2. Who was very happy?
3. What did Bobby tell his class?
4. What did Bobby do with the jar of caterpillars?
5. What did the class decide to do with the caterpillars?

SPRING CLEANING

INSTRUCTOR'S WORKSHEET

INSTRUCTOR'S DIRECTIONS:

Before beginning, the instructor should give each student the worksheet that corresponds to the instructor's worksheet. Before reading Story #1, the instructor should ask the students to listen carefully to three questions and remember the information as the story is read. The instructor then reads the story aloud. After the story is read, the instructor asks the same three questions along with two additional questions for the students to answer aloud. Their large picture should provide visual clues. In Story #2, the same process is repeated, keeping in mind that the questions and story do not refer directly to the picture.

SPRING CLEANING

Story #1 (Pictured)

Things to remember:

1. What day is today?
2. What does Susie's mother want her to do?
3. What did Susie's mother give her to help her dust the house?

Today is the first day of spring. Susie's mother has a long list of chores to do. The first chore on Susie's list is dusting. Her mother gives her a feather duster to make the job easier. Susie starts to dust the furniture. What a mess! The dust goes everywhere. It is going to take her a long time to dust. She is glad she has a feather duster to use.

Questions:

1. What day is today?
2. Does Susie's mother have a long list of chores?
3. What does Susie's mother want her to do?
4. What did Susie's mother give her to help her dust the house?
5. What is Susie dusting?

Story #2: (Not Pictured)

Things to remember:

1. How long did Susie dust the house?
2. What did she do after she dusted the house?
3. What was Susie's surprise?

Susie dusted the house all morning. She even helped her mother vacuum and wash the windows. Her mother was very proud of her. She gave Susie a hug and said she had a surprise for her. She told Susie to run upstairs and wash her face and hands because they were going to the ice-cream parlor for banana splits.

Questions:

1. How long did Susie dust the house?
2. What did Susie do after she dusted the house?
3. Did Susie's mother give her a hug or a penny?
4. What did Susie do before her surprise?
5. What was Susie's surprise?

PLAYING HIDE-AND-SEEK

INSTRUCTOR'S WORKSHEET

PLAYING HIDE-AND-SEEK

Story #1 (Pictured)

Things to remember:

1. Why couldn't Tommy and Billy play outside?
2. Who decided to hide first?
3. Where did Tommy hide?

It was a rainy day so Billy and Tommy could not play outside. They decided to play hide-and-seek in the house. It was Tommy's turn to hide. He thought and thought about the best place to hide so Billy would not find him. He decided to hide in his father's office. He crawled under the desk and kept very quiet. He knew it would take Billy a long time to find him.

Questions:

1. Why couldn't Tommy and Billy play outside?
2. What kind of game did they decide to play?
3. Who hid first?
4. Where did Tommy hide?
5. Why did he keep quiet?

Story #2: (Not Pictured)

Things to remember:

1. How long did Tommy hide under the desk?
2. What happened when he peeked over the desk?
3. How did Billy find Tommy?

Tommy hid under the desk for a long time. He peeked over the top of the desk to see if Billy was coming. When he did, he knocked over the pencil holder on the desk. It made a loud noise when all of the pencils and pens fell on the floor. Billy came running through the door. He heard all the noise and that is how he found Tommy.

Questions:

1. How long did Tommy hide under the desk?
2. What did Tommy do to see if Billy was coming?
3. What happened when he peeked over the desk?
4. What fell out of the pencil holder?
5. How did Billy find Tommy?

FEEDING THE DUCKS IN THE PARK

INSTRUCTOR'S WORKSHEET

INSTRUCTOR'S DIRECTIONS:

Before beginning, the instructor should give each student the worksheet that corresponds to the instructor's worksheet. Before reading Story #1, the instructor should ask the students to listen carefully to three questions and remember the information as the story is read. The instructor then reads the story aloud. After the story is read, the instructor asks the same three questions along with two additional questions for the students to answer aloud. Their large picture should provide visual clues. In Story #2, the same process is repeated, keeping in mind that the questions and story do not refer directly to the picture.

FEEDING THE DUCKS IN THE PARK

Story #1 (Pictured)

Things to remember:

1. Where did Lisa and her mother go?
2. What did Lisa take with her to the park?
3. How many ducks did Lisa see?

Lisa and her mother went to the park. Lisa took a bag of bread crumbs so she could feed the ducks. When they arrived at the park, they went straight to the pond. Lisa saw a mother duck and three baby ducks. She took out her bag of crumbs and threw some on the ground. The ducks gathered around her feet and began to eat the crumbs.

Questions:

1. Where did Lisa and her mother go?
2. What did Lisa take with her to the park?
3. What did Lisa do with the bread crumbs?
4. How many ducks did Lisa see?
5. What did the mother duck and the baby ducks do?

Story #2: (Not Pictured)

Things to remember:

1. Where did Lisa go after she fed the ducks?
2. What did Lisa want to do at the playground?
3. Why did the bread crumbs fall out of the bag?

After Lisa and her mother fed the ducks, they walked to the playground. Lisa wanted to play on the swings. Lisa did not know that her bag of bread crumbs had a hole in it. She was leaving a trail of bread crumbs. Lisa heard a quacking sound behind her. She turned around and saw the mother duck with her three baby ducks. They were following the trail of bread crumbs.

Questions:

1. Where did Lisa go after she fed the ducks?
2. What did Lisa want to do at the playground?
3. Why did the bread crumbs fall out of the bag?
4. What sound did Lisa hear?
5. What was following Lisa?

CARVING A JACK-O'-LANTERN

INSTRUCTOR'S WORKSHEET

INSTRUCTOR'S DIRECTIONS:

Before beginning, the instructor should give each student the worksheet that corresponds to the instructor's worksheet. Before reading Story #1, the instructor should ask the students to listen carefully to three questions and remember the information as the story is read. The instructor then reads the story aloud. After the story is read, the instructor asks the same three questions along with two additional questions for the students to answer aloud. Their large picture should provide visual clues. In Story #2, the same process is repeated, keeping in mind that the questions and story do not refer directly to the picture.

CARVING A JACK-O'-LANTERN

Story #1 (Pictured)

Things to remember:

1. What is special about tomorrow?
2. What is Betsy making?
3. What kind of face did Betsy carve?

Tomorrow is Halloween. Betsy is making a jack-o'-lantern to put in the living room window. Her father bought a pumpkin for Betsy to carve. It was big and orange. Betsy used her mother's kitchen knife to carve a hole in the top of the pumpkin. Next she cleaned the inside and carved a scary face in the pumpkin. When she finished, she put the pumpkin in the window.

Questions:

1. What is special about tomorrow?
2. What is Betsy making?
3. What color is the pumpkin?
4. What kind of face did Betsy carve?
5. Where did Betsy put the pumpkin when she was done?

Story #2: (Not Pictured)

Things to remember:

1. What did Betsy use to light the candle in the pumpkin?
2. What did the jack-o'-lantern look like?
3. What did Betsy put on?

On Halloween night, Betsy lit the candle in the jack-o'-lantern with a match. She went outside and looked at the pumpkin sitting in the window. It looked like a scary monster. She ran back inside and put on her Halloween costume so she could go trick-or-treating. While she walked through the neighborhood, she looked to see if anyone else had a jack-o'-lantern as scary as hers.

Questions:

1. What did Betsy use to light the candle in the pumpkin?
2. What did the jack-o'-lantern look like?
3. What did Betsy put on?
4. Where did Betsy walk to trick-or-treat?
5. What did Betsy look for?

BUILDING A TREE HOUSE

INSTRUCTOR'S WORKSHEET

INSTRUCTOR'S DIRECTIONS:

Before beginning, the instructor should give each student the worksheet that corresponds to the instructor's worksheet. Before reading Story #1, the instructor should ask the students to listen carefully to three questions and remember the information as the story is read. The instructor then reads the story aloud. After the story is read, the instructor asks the same three questions along with two additional questions for the students to answer aloud. Their large picture should provide visual clues. In Story #2, the same process is repeated, keeping in mind that the questions and story do not refer directly to the picture.

BUILDING A TREE HOUSE

Story #1 (Pictured)

Things to remember:

1. What did Jimmy want to build?
2. Where did Jimmy get the wood to build the tree house?
3. What did Jimmy use to cut the wood?

Jimmy wanted to build a tree house. There was a big tree in his backyard that was perfect for one. His father took him to the lumber store to buy some wood. They brought the wood home and put it in his dad's workroom. Jimmy used a saw to cut the pieces of wood. When he was finished, he had enough wood to build a tree house.

Questions:

1. What did Jimmy want to build?
2. Where did he want to build the tree house?
3. Where did Jimmy get the wood to build the tree house?
4. Where did Jimmy cut the wood?
5. What did Jimmy use to cut the wood?

Story #2: (Not Pictured)

Things to remember:

1. What did Jimmy put the wood in after he cut it?
2. How did Jimmy get the wood up the tree?
3. What part of the tree house did he build first?

After Jimmy cut the wood, he loaded it in his wagon. He also put a hammer and some nails in the wagon. Then he pulled the wagon to the big tree in his backyard. He used a ladder to carry the wood up the tree. He nailed the pieces of wood together to make the floor. Then he built the sides and the roof. By the end of the day, Jimmy had a new tree house.

Questions:

1. What did Jimmy put the wood in after he cut it?
2. What else did he put in the wagon?
3. How did Jimmy get the wood up the tree?
4. What part of the tree house did he build first?
5. How long did it take Jimmy to build his tree house?

LUCY TAKES A NAP

INSTRUCTOR'S WORKSHEET

INSTRUCTOR'S DIRECTIONS:

Before beginning, the instructor should give each student the worksheet that corresponds to the instructor's worksheet. Before reading Story #1, the instructor should ask the students to listen carefully to three questions and remember the information as the story is read. The instructor then reads the story aloud. After the story is read, the instructor asks the same three questions along with two additional questions for the students to answer aloud. Their large picture should provide visual clues. In Story #2, the same process is repeated, keeping in mind that the questions and story do not refer directly to the picture.

LUCY TAKES A NAP

Story #1 (Pictured)

Things to remember:

1. Why was Lucy tired?
2. What did Lucy decide to do?
3. What took a nap with Lucy?

Lucy had a very busy morning helping her mother clean the house. She was so tired she decided to take a nap. She went to her bedroom and pulled down the covers on her bed. Then she climbed in the bed. She fell asleep in two minutes. Even her cat, Fuzzy, was tired. Fuzzy jumped on top of the bed and fell asleep too.

Questions:

1. Why was Lucy tired?
2. What did Lucy decide to do?
3. What room did Lucy take her nap in?
4. Did it take Lucy a long time to fall asleep?
5. What took a nap with Lucy?

Story #2: (Not Pictured)

Things to remember:

1. Was Lucy tired when she woke up?
2. What did Lucy want to do after her nap?
3. What kind of game did Lucy and her friends play?

When Lucy woke up from her nap she wasn't tired anymore. She decided she wanted to go out and play. She put on her coat and ran outside to be with her friends. She saw Nancy and Sally at the playground. Lucy decided to jump rope with them. She was happy she took a nap because she was able to jump rope the highest.

Questions:

1. Was Lucy tired when she woke up?
2. What did Lucy want to do after her nap?
3. What did she put on when she went outside?
4. Which friends did Lucy see outside?
5. What kind of game did Lucy and her friends play?

STUDENT WORKSHEET

GETTING READY FOR A SNOWBALL FIGHT

INSTRUCTOR'S WORKSHEET

INSTRUCTOR'S DIRECTIONS:

Before beginning, the instructor should give each student the worksheet that corresponds to the instructor's worksheet. Before reading Story #1, the instructor should ask the students to listen carefully to three questions and remember the information as the story is read. The instructor then reads the story aloud. After the story is read, the instructor asks the same three questions along with two additional questions for the students to answer aloud. Their large picture should provide visual clues. In Story #2, the same process is repeated, keeping in mind that the questions and story do not refer directly to the picture.

GETTING READY FOR A SNOWBALL FIGHT

Story #1 (Pictured)

Things to remember:

1. What did Debbie and her friends want to do?
2. What tool did Debbie use to build her fort?
3. What did Debbie put behind the wall?

Debbie and her friends are going to have a snowball fight. They each built a fort made of snow. Debbie used a shovel to build her fort. In the middle of the wall she made a "look out" notch. She made a flag out of a stick and a scarf and stuck it in one side of the fort. She made a lot of snowballs and put them behind the wall. She was ready for the snowball fight.

Questions:

1. What did Debbie and her friends want to do?
2. What tool did Debbie use to build her fort?
3. What is her fort made of?
4. What did Debbie use to make the flag?
5. What did Debbie put behind the wall?

Story #2: (Not Pictured)

Things to remember:

1. Did Debbie and her friends have lots of fun?
2. When did they stop throwing snowballs?
3. Why didn't they throw snowballs at anyone's head?

Debbie and her friends had lots of fun. They threw snowballs at each other until all the snowballs were gone. They were very careful not to throw the snowballs at anyone's head because it would be dangerous. Everyone was very cold so they stopped throwing snowballs. Instead, they decided to go to Debbie's house for hot chocolate.

Questions:

1. Did Debbie and her friends have lots of fun?
2. What were they throwing?
3. Why didn't they throw snowballs at anyone's head?
4. Why did they stop throwing snowballs?
5. Where did they go for hot chocolate?

GEORGE HAD AN ACCIDENT

INSTRUCTOR'S WORKSHEET

INSTRUCTOR'S DIRECTIONS:

Before beginning, the instructor should give each student the worksheet that corresponds to the instructor's worksheet. Before reading Story #1, the instructor should ask the students to listen carefully to three questions and remember the information as the story is read. The instructor then reads the story aloud. After the story is read, the instructor asks the same three questions along with two additional questions for the students to answer aloud. Their large picture should provide visual clues. In Story #2, the same process is repeated, keeping in mind that the questions and story do not refer directly to the picture.

GEORGE HAD AN ACCIDENT

Story #1 (Pictured)

Things to remember:

1. What was George making for breakfast?
2. What was wrong with the lid on the jelly jar?
3. What happened when the lid came off?

George was making jelly toast for breakfast. He took the jelly out of the refrigerator. He tried to open the jar but the lid was stuck. He turned the lid as hard as he could. All of a sudden, the lid came off and George dropped the jar. Jelly spilled all over the front of George's shirt and the kitchen counter. His sister, Mary, tried to wipe the jelly off his shirt with a wet cloth.

Questions:

1. What was George making for breakfast?
2. Where was the jar of jelly?
3. What was wrong with the lid on the jelly jar?
4. What happened when the lid came off?
5. Where did the jelly spill?

Story #2: (Not Pictured)

Things to remember:

1. What was left on the shirt after Mary wiped off the jelly?
2. What did Mary do with the shirt?
3. Why was George happy?

After Mary wiped the jelly off George's shirt, there was a big purple stain on it. She decided to wash George's shirt in the washing machine. George took off his shirt and gave it to Mary. She put it in the washing machine and added lots of soap powder. In a few minutes the wash was through. Mary took George's shirt out of the machine. The jelly stain was gone. George was very happy.

Questions:

1. What was left on the shirt after Mary wiped off the jelly?
2. What did Mary do with the shirt?
3. What else did Mary put in the washing machine?
4. How long did the washing machine run?
5. Why was George happy?

LISA HITS A HOME RUN

INSTRUCTOR'S WORKSHEET

INSTRUCTOR'S DIRECTIONS:

Before beginning, the instructor should give each student the worksheet that corresponds to the instructor's worksheet. Before reading Story #1, the instructor should ask the students to listen carefully to three questions and remember the information as the story is read. The instructor then reads the story aloud. After the story is read, the instructor asks the same three questions along with two additional questions for the students to answer aloud. Their large picture should provide visual clues. In Story #2, the same process is repeated, keeping in mind that the questions and story do not refer directly to the picture.

LISA HITS A HOME RUN

Story #1 (Pictured)

Things to remember:

1. What kind of team does Lisa play on?
2. What kind of special clothes is Lisa wearing?
3. How many times did Lisa miss the ball?

Lisa is on the Ladybug softball team. She is wearing a new hat, uniform and sneakers. Lisa is the first person to bat the ball. She stands at home plate and waits for the pitcher to throw the ball. She misses the first ball and the second ball. The third time, she hit the ball. She hits it so hard it flies through the air above everyone's head. Nobody is able to catch the ball. Lisa hits a home run.

Questions:

1. What kind of team does Lisa play on?
2. What is the name of the team?
3. What kind of special clothes is Lisa wearing?
4. How many times did Lisa miss the ball?
5. What happened when Lisa hit the ball?

Story #2: (Not Pictured)

Things to remember:

1. Who won the softball game?
2. Where did the team go after the game?
3. What did Lisa order?

Lisa's team won the softball game. They beat the Caterpillar team. After the game, the coach took all the girls for ice cream. Lisa ordered her favorite, a banana split. It had three kinds of ice cream - vanilla, chocolate and strawberry. On top of the ice cream there were bananas, whipped cream, chocolate syrup and a cherry. It was the best dessert of all.

Questions:

1. Who won the softball game?
2. What was the name of the other team?
3. Where did the team go after the game?
4. What kind of ice cream was in Lisa's dessert?
5. What did Lisa order?

STUDENT WORKSHEET

HELPING DAD RAKE LEAVES

INSTRUCTOR'S WORKSHEET

INSTRUCTOR'S DIRECTIONS:

Before beginning, the instructor should give each student the worksheet that corresponds to the instructor's worksheet. Before reading Story #1, the instructor should ask the students to listen carefully to three questions and remember the information as the story is read. The instructor then reads the story aloud. After the story is read, the instructor asks the same three questions along with two additional questions for the students to answer aloud. Their large picture should provide visual clues. In Story #2, the same process is repeated, keeping in mind that the questions and story do not refer directly to the picture.

HELPING DAD RAKE LEAVES

Story #1 (Pictured)

Things to remember:

1. What day is today?
2. What are Randy and his dad going to do?
3. What did Randy use to carry the leaves to the woods?

Today is Saturday. Randy's dad wants to rake leaves and he needs Randy's help. There are many leaves on the ground. Randy and his dad rake the leaves in small piles in the yard. Then Randy puts the leaves in a basket. He carries the basket into the woods and dumps the leaves in a big pile. He goes back and forth carrying baskets of leaves until all the piles are gone.

Questions:

1. What day is today?
2. What are Randy and his dad going to do?
3. Where did they rake the little piles of leaves?
4. What did Randy use to carry the leaves to the woods?
5. Is the pile of leaves in the woods big or little?

Story #2: (Not Pictured)

Things to remember:

1. Why did Randy get a reward?
2. Where did Randy and his dad eat?
3. What are Randy's favorite things to eat?

Randy and his dad finished raking the leaves. As a reward for being a good helper, Randy's dad took him to lunch. Randy picked his favorite place, Mr. Bobo's Hamburger House. He ordered his favorite meal: a hamburger, french fries and a chocolate milk shake. Randy told his dad he would help him next Saturday if they could go out to lunch again.

Questions:

1. Why did Randy get a reward?
2. Who picked out the place to eat?
3. What was the name of Randy's favorite place?
4. Did Randy eat a hamburger or a cheeseburger?
5. Why did Randy want to help his dad again next Saturday?

WALKING IN THE RAIN

INSTRUCTOR'S WORKSHEET

INSTRUCTOR'S DIRECTIONS:

Before beginning, the instructor should give each student the worksheet that corresponds to the instructor's worksheet. Before reading Story #1, the instructor should ask the students to listen carefully to three questions and remember the information as the story is read. The instructor then reads the story aloud. After the story is read, the instructor asks the same three questions along with two additional questions for the students to answer aloud. Their large picture should provide visual clues. In Story #2, the same process is repeated, keeping in mind that the questions and story do not refer directly to the picture.

WALKING IN THE RAIN

Story #1 (Pictured)

Things to remember:

1. What kind of day is it?
2. Where are Sara and Sam going?
3. What are Sara and Sam wearing to keep dry?

It is a rainy day. Sara and Sam are going to Jill's house to play. Their mother said they could walk to Jill's house but they would need to put on their rain clothes. Sara and Sam put on their raincoats and boots. Their raincoats had snaps in the front to keep them closed and hoods to keep their heads dry. Now Sara and Sam can walk to Jill's house and not get wet.

Questions:

1. What kind of day is it?
2. Where are Sara and Sam going?
3. What are Sara and Sam wearing to keep dry?
4. What keeps their raincoats closed?
5. What are Sara and Sam wearing on their feet?

Story #2: (Not Pictured)

Things to remember:

1. Where did Sara and Sam put their wet clothes?
2. Were Sara and Sam wet or cold?
3. What did Jill's mother fix to drink?

When Sara and Sam reached Jill's house, they put their wet coats and boots in the laundry room. Sara and Sam were dry but very cold. Jill's mother fixed some hot chocolate. She put marshmallows in each of their cups. The hot chocolate warmed them up. When they were through, they went into the family room to play games and watch television. They had lots of fun.

Questions:

1. Where did Sara and Sam put their wet clothes?
2. Were Sara and Sam wet or cold?
3. What did Jill's mother fix to drink?
4. What did she put in their hot chocolate?
5. What did the children do after they finished drinking their hot chocolate?

BUDDY HAS A BICYCLE ACCIDENT

INSTRUCTOR'S WORKSHEET

INSTRUCTOR'S DIRECTIONS:

Before beginning, the instructor should give each student the worksheet that corresponds to the instructor's worksheet. Before reading Story #1, the instructor should ask the students to listen carefully to three questions and remember the information as the story is read. The instructor then reads the story aloud. After the story is read, the instructor asks the same three questions along with two additional questions for the students to answer aloud. Their large picture should provide visual clues. In Story #2, the same process is repeated, keeping in mind that the questions and story do not refer directly to the picture.

BUDDY HAS A BICYCLE ACCIDENT

Story #1 (Pictured)

Things to remember:

1. Where was Buddy riding his bicycle?
2. Who else was riding a bicycle?
3. What happened when Buddy was not paying attention?

Buddy was riding his bicycle through the park. While he was riding, he was talking to his friend, Joe. Buddy was talking too much and did not pay attention to where he was going. He did not see a rock in the road. Bam! His bicycle hit the rock. Buddy's hands came off the handlebars and he fell off his bicycle.

Questions:

1. Where was Buddy riding his bicycle?
2. Who else was riding a bicycle?
3. Why was Buddy not paying attention?
4. What happened when Buddy was not paying attention?
5. Why did Buddy fall off his bicycle?

Story #2: (Not Pictured)

Things to remember:

1. What happened when Buddy fell off his bicycle?
2. Did he tear his shirt or his pants?
3. What happened to Buddy's bicycle?

When Buddy fell off his bicycle, he landed on his hands and knees. He scraped both of his hands and tore his pants. He got up slowly and looked at his bicycle. The bicycle had a flat tire and bent handlebars. Buddy picked up his bicycle and slowly started walking home. He asked his mother to fix his cuts and bruises and asked his dad to fix his bicycle.

Questions:

1. What happened when Buddy fell off his bicycle?
2. What happened to Buddy's hands?
3. Did he tear his shirt or his pants?
4. What happened to Buddy's bicycle?
5. Who did Buddy ask to fix his bicycle when he got home?

STUDENT WORKSHEET

BOBBY PICKS UP THE MAIL

INSTRUCTOR'S WORKSHEET

INSTRUCTOR'S DIRECTIONS:

Before beginning, the instructor should give each student the worksheet that corresponds to the instructor's worksheet. Before reading Story #1, the instructor should ask the students to listen carefully to three questions and remember the information as the story is read. The instructor then reads the story aloud. After the story is read, the instructor asks the same three questions along with two additional questions for the students to answer aloud. Their large picture should provide visual clues. In Story #2, the same process is repeated, keeping in mind that the questions and story do not refer directly to the picture.

BOBBY PICKS UP THE MAIL

Story #1 (Pictured)

Things to remember:

1. What did Bobby's mother ask him to do?
2. Where was the mailbox?
3. Were there a lot or a few letters in the mailbox?

Bobby's mother asked him to walk to the mailbox to get the mail. Bobby took his dog, Spot, with him. The mailbox was at the end of the driveway. It was a long walk. There were a lot of letters in it. Bobby took some of the letters out of the mailbox and gave them to Spot to carry. Bobby carried the rest of the letters.

Questions:

1. What did Bobby's mother ask him to do?
2. Where was the mailbox?
3. What was in the mailbox?
4. Were there a lot or a few letters in the mailbox?
5. Did Bobby have help carrying the letters?

Story #2: (Not Pictured)

Things to remember:

1. What did Bobby give to his mother?
2. What did Spot do with the letters in his mouth?
3. Where did Bobby and his mother chase Spot?

Bobby gave the letters to his mother. Spot did not want to give up the letters in his mouth. He ran away with them. Bobby and his mother chased Spot up and down the driveway and all over the yard. Bobby kept yelling to Spot, "Stop, Spot!," but Spot wouldn't listen. When Spot was tired, he stopped to rest. Bobby grabbed him and took the letters. They were wet but all in one piece.

Questions:

1. What did Bobby give to his mother?
2. What did Spot do with the letters in his mouth?
3. Where did Bobby and his mother chase Spot?
4. What did Bobby yell at Spot?
5. What happened when Spot became tired?

CINDY GOES CAMPING

INSTRUCTOR'S WORKSHEET

INSTRUCTOR'S DIRECTIONS:

Before beginning, the instructor should give each student the worksheet that corresponds to the instructor's worksheet. Before reading Story #1, the instructor should ask the students to listen carefully to three questions and remember the information as the story is read. The instructor then reads the story aloud. After the story is read, the instructor asks the same three questions along with two additional questions for the students to answer aloud. Their large picture should provide visual clues. In Story #2, the same process is repeated, keeping in mind that the questions and story do not refer directly to the picture.

CINDY GOES CAMPING

Story #1 (Pictured)

Things to remember:

1. Where are Cindy and her friends going?
2. Who packed Cindy's backpack for her?
3. Where did Cindy put the backpack?

Cindy and her friends are going camping. Cindy's mom packed everything she will need in her backpack. She packed some food, a sleeping bag and a little tent. She also put in a flashlight to use at night. Cindy put the backpack on her back. The backpack was heavy so she held it by the straps on her shoulders. Cindy was ready to go camping.

Questions:

1. Where are Cindy and her friends going?
2. Who packed Cindy's backpack for her?
3. What did her mother pack in the backpack for Cindy to sleep in?
4. What will Cindy use to see at night?
5. What did Cindy do so the backpack would not feel so heavy?

Story #2: (Not Pictured)

Things to remember:

1. Where did Cindy and her friends put their tent?
2. What did they put inside the tent?
3. What did they eat as they sat around the pretend campfire?

Cindy and her friends found a place in the woods to put the tent. They took the tent out of Cindy's backpack and set it up. Then they put their sleeping bags in the tent. They built a pretend campfire. They sat around it and ate their peanut butter and jelly sandwiches. Soon it began to get dark. The girls took out their flashlights and told ghost stories until it was time to go to sleep.

Questions:

1. Where did Cindy and her friends put their tent?
2. What did they put inside the tent?
3. What did they pretend to build?
4. What did they eat as they sat around the pretend campfire?
5. What did they do when it got dark?

BLOWING BUBBLES

INSTRUCTOR'S WORKSHEET

INSTRUCTOR'S DIRECTIONS:

Before beginning, the instructor should give each student the worksheet that corresponds to the instructor's worksheet. Before reading Story #1, the instructor should ask the students to listen carefully to three questions and remember the information as the story is read. The instructor then reads the story aloud. After the story is read, the instructor asks the same three questions along with two additional questions for the students to answer aloud. Their large picture should provide visual clues. In Story #2, the same process is repeated, keeping in mind that the questions and story do not refer directly to the picture.

BLOWING BUBBLES

Story #1 (Pictured)

Things to remember:

1. Why did Lisa get a new jar of bubbles?
2. What color were the bubbles?
3. What size were the bubbles?

Lisa got a new jar of bubbles for her birthday. Her mother told her she could not blow bubbles in the house, so she took them outside. The bubbles in the jar were pink. Lisa dipped the wand into the jar and blew through it. Bubbles of all sizes came out of the wand. Some were big and some were little. Lisa watched all of them float away high in the sky.

Questions:

1. Why did Lisa get a new jar of bubbles?
2. Was Lisa allowed to blow bubbles inside the house?
3. What color were the bubbles?
4. What size were the bubbles?
5. Where did the bubbles go?

Story #2: (Not Pictured)

Things to remember:

1. After lunch, where did Lisa take her jar of bubbles?
2. Where did the children sit to blow bubbles?
3. What did all the bubbles look like?

After lunch, Lisa took her jar of bubbles over to Patty's house. Patty also had a jar of bubbles. Lisa and Patty sat on the steps and blew bubbles. They blew so many bubbles it looked like a bubble factory. Some of the bubbles blew over to Mr. Green's yard. Mr. Green's dog, Buffy, barked and jumped at the bubbles. Lisa and Patty laughed.

Questions:

1. After lunch, where did Lisa take her jar of bubbles?
2. Where did the children sit to blow bubbles?
3. What did all the bubbles look like?
4. Where did the bubbles blow?
5. What started barking at the bubbles?

PLAYING MAKE-BELIEVE

INSTRUCTOR'S WORKSHEET

INSTRUCTOR'S DIRECTIONS:

Before beginning, the instructor should give each student the worksheet that corresponds to the instructor's worksheet. Before reading Story #1, the instructor should ask the students to listen carefully to three questions and remember the information as the story is read. The instructor then reads the story aloud. After the story is read, the instructor asks the same three questions along with two additional questions for the students to answer aloud. Their large picture should provide visual clues. In Story #2, the same process is repeated, keeping in mind that the questions and story do not refer directly to the picture.

PLAYING MAKE-BELIEVE

Story #1 (Pictured)

Things to remember:

1. What were Johnny and his friends doing?
2. What were the children pretending to be?
3. Why did the children think Johnny was a real dog?

Johnny and his friends were playing make-believe. They were pretending to be animals. Johnny decided he would be a dog. He ran around his yard and barked just like his dog, Spot. The other children laughed but didn't think Johnny was a very good dog. Then Johnny crawled inside of Spot's doghouse, stuck his head out the door and barked again. Then he looked like a real dog.

Questions:

1. What were Johnny and his friends doing?
2. What were the children pretending to be?
3. What was Johnny pretending to be?
4. What kind of sound did Johnny make?
5. Why did the children think Johnny was a real dog?

Story #2: (Not Pictured)

Things to remember:

1. Why was Spot unhappy?
2. What did Spot do when Johnny would not come out of the doghouse?
3. How many real dogs were in the doghouse?

The children laughed at Johnny in the doghouse. Spot was not happy. He wanted to go in the doghouse. Spot ran around the doghouse and barked at Johnny. When Johnny would not come out, Spot crawled in the doghouse with him. Just like Johnny, Spot stuck his head outside the door and started barking at the children. Everyone laughed at the real dog and the pretend dog.

Questions:

1. Why was Spot unhappy?
2. Why did Spot bark at Johnny?
3. What did Spot do when Johnny would not come out of the doghouse?
4. What did Spot do in the doghouse?
5. How many real dogs were in the doghouse?

DUSTING THE FURNITURE

INSTRUCTOR'S WORKSHEET

INSTRUCTOR'S DIRECTIONS:

Before beginning, the instructor should give each student the worksheet that corresponds to the instructor's worksheet. Before reading Story #1, the instructor should ask the students to listen carefully to three questions and remember the information as the story is read. The instructor then reads the story aloud. After the story is read, the instructor asks the same three questions along with two additional questions for the students to answer aloud. Their large picture should provide visual clues. In Story #2, the same process is repeated, keeping in mind that the questions and story do not refer directly to the picture.

DUSTING THE FURNITURE

Story #1 (Pictured)

Things to remember:

1. How is Mary helping her mother?
2. What is she using to clean the table?
3. What is the last thing Mary polished?

Mary is helping her mother with the housework. Mary's job is to dust and polish the furniture. Her mother gave her a clean rag and a bottle of furniture polish. Mary cleaned the kitchen table and chairs and all the dining room furniture. Then she cleaned the living room. When she was done, she decided to clean the desk in her playroom. Her desk is her favorite piece of furniture so she polished it very carefully.

Questions:

1. How is Mary helping her mother?
2. What is she using to clean the table?
3. What rooms did Mary clean?
4. What piece of furniture did Mary polish last?
5. Why did Mary polish her desk very carefully?

Story #2: (Not Pictured)

Things to remember:

1. What did Mary do before she dusted and polished her desk?
2. Where did she put all the things from her desk?
3. Why did she quickly pick them up?

Before Mary dusted and polished her desk, she had to take everything off it. She put all the things on the floor. There was a lamp, pencil holder, crayons, ruler and lots of paper. Because Mary's mother was waiting to vacuum the floor, Mary had to pile everything back on the desk very quickly. Now, the desk looked the same as before she started.

Questions:

1. What did Mary do before she dusted and polished her desk?
2. Where did she put all the things from her desk?
3. Name some of the things that were on Mary's desk.
4. Why did she quickly pick them up?
5. Did the desk look the same as before?

STUDENT WORKSHEET

SCUBA DIVING

INSTRUCTOR'S WORKSHEET

INSTRUCTOR'S DIRECTIONS:

Before beginning, the instructor should give each student the worksheet that corresponds to the instructor's worksheet. Before reading Story #1, the instructor should ask the students to listen carefully to three questions and remember the information as the story is read. The instructor then reads the story aloud. After the story is read, the instructor asks the same three questions along with two additional questions for the students to answer aloud. Their large picture should provide visual clues. In Story #2, the same process is repeated, keeping in mind that the questions and story do not refer directly to the picture.

SCUBA DIVING

Story #1 (Pictured)

Things to remember:

1. What are Jane and John doing?
2. Why are they wearing masks?
3. Which fish is John pointing at?

Jane and John are scuba diving. They are wearing masks to see better and fins on their feet so they can swim faster. When they breath through their masks, a lot of little bubbles come out. Jane and John see two fish in the water. One is a big fish and the other is a striped fish. John is pointing at the big fish.

Questions:

1. What are John and Jane doing?
2. Why are they wearing masks?
3. Why are they wearing fins on their feet?
4. What comes out of their masks when they breath?
5. Which fish is John pointing at?

Story #2: (Not Pictured)

Things to remember:

1. Why do Jane and John like to scuba dive?
2. What kind of fish do they see?
3. Where do they see crabs?

Jane and John like to scuba dive because they see many different things in the ocean. They see big fish, little fish, striped fish and spotted fish. Sometimes they see crabs crawling on the bottom of the ocean. They don't go near the crabs because crabs pinch with their claws. Jane and John also collect shells to bring home to their mother.

Questions:

1. Why do Jane and John like to scuba dive?
2. What kind of fish do they see?
3. Where do they see crabs?
4. Why don't they go near the crabs?
5. What do they collect to bring home to their mother?